Cutting Skills

Photocopiable activities to improve scissor technique

Original concept, design and content by
Mark and Katy Hill

Permission to photocopy

This book contains materials which may be reproduced by photocopier or other means for use by the purchaser. This permission is granted on the understanding that these copies will be used within the educational establishment of the purchaser. This book and all its contents remain copyright. Copies may be made without reference to the publisher or the licensing scheme for the making of photocopies operated by the Publishers' Licensing Agency.

The rights of Mark and Katy Hill to be identified as authors of this work have been asserted by them in accordance with sections 77 and 78 of the Copyright, Designs and Patents Act 1988.

Cutting Skills
MT00565
ISBN-13: 978 1 85503 349 8

First published 2002
Reprinted 2003, 2004 (twice), 2005, 2006, 2007, 2009, 2010, 2011, 2012, 2013, 2014, 2015, 2016

Printed in the UK for LDA
LDA Pintail Close, Victoria Business Park, Nottingham, NG4 2SG UK

Table of Contents

Teacher's Notes.. 4

Instructions.. 5

Cutting to a Point.. 8

Cutting Straight Lines... 11

Cutting Curved Lines.. 16

Cutting Simple Objects.. 23

Cutting and Assembling... 28

Cutting Along a Broken Line......................................32

Cutting Along a Dotted Line..................................... 35

Cutting and Assembling More Complex Shapes...................... 38

Cutting Within Shapes... 45

Teacher's Notes

The activities provided in this book are intended to develop children's hand–eye coordination, motor skills and scissor technique. To assist this development the thickness of the cutting line decreases as the activities become more advanced. Children can be matched to an appropriate starting point in the book once their areas of difficulty have been identified. To make the activities easier they can be enlarged and the cutting lines thickened with a marker pen. Each activity provides an opportunity for teaching and assessment.

Teaching points

- Suitable scissors should be given to children, especially those who are left-handed.
- Children should be encouraged to position their page appropriately and to cut in a suitable direction.
- Allow plenty of practice in cutting to a specific point to help children confidently estimate distance and the length of the cut.
- Before cutting out an object itself children should cut away any excess paper.
- Children should be directed to cut around curves by moving the paper with their non-scissor hand.
- When cutting out a shape within a shape, children should make a slight fold along one of the dotted lines and then make a small cut on the fold. From here they can cut outwards along the dotted lines to the edge of the shape and then cut around it. Alternatively, they can begin by making a small hole on the cutting line with a sharp pencil. Push the pencil through the sheet into a ball of play clay on a table.
- When children need to assemble a number of components a small picture is supplied as a guide. The children may need reminding to keep this for reference.

Safety points

When using scissors the following points should be followed:

- Children should be supervised at all times when using scissors.
- When carrying scissors children should hold them with the closed blades in the palm of their hand and with the handles uppermost.
- Children should put scissors down before using objects they have made.
- Encourage children to be careful of paper cuts.

Instructions

Cutting to a Point

Activity 1 Place mat
Children cut out the place mat. Cut along the lines to the black dots to fringe the edges of the mat.

Activity 2 Cutting staircase
Children cut out the rectangle and cut along the staircase lines to the black dots.

Activity 3 Bookmark
Children decorate and cut out the bookmarks. They should be precise and cut along the exact line lengths.

Cutting Straight Lines

Activity 4 Square shape family
Children decorate the square shape family and cut them out. Ask the children to sort the squares according to size and give them each a name.

Activity 5 Robot
Children decorate and cut out the robot. List the tasks their robot would do on the back of it.

Activity 6 Triangle shape family
Children cut out the triangle shape family. Investigate the different attributes of each of them.

Activity 7 Spikies
Children decorate and cut out the Spikies. Using a felt tip draw some more complex Spikies for a partner to cut out.

Activity 8 Saw
Children cut out the saw following the zigzag line accurately. List other items with zigzag lines on the back of the saw.

Cutting Curved Lines

Activity 9 Curved line puzzle
Children decorate and cut out the puzzle. They try to reassemble it. When cutting, encourage correct positioning of the puzzle to account for left/right-handedness.

Activity 10 Design a plate
Children investigate different plate designs. They use the template to design their own and cut it out.

Activity 11 Circle shape family
Children decorate and cut out the circle shape family. They can order them by size and give them each a name.

Activity 12 Snakes
Children decorate and cut out the snakes. These can be placed on a similar background so that they are camouflaged.

Activity 13 Blobby buddies
Children decorate and cut out the blobby buddies. Using a felt tip they can draw some more complex buddies for a partner to cut out.

Activities 14/15 Spiral snakes
Children decorate and cut out the spiral snake. There is a snake for both left and right-handed children. Attach a thread to the snake's tail and hang it above a heater, where it will spin.

Cutting Simple Objects

Activity 16 Design a T-shirt
Children design a T-shirt and cut it out. Each child's T-shirt can have their face on it and be used as part of a display.

Activity 17 Picture frame
Children decorate and cut out the picture frame along the thick cutting line. (More able children can cut along the thinner line.) They draw a picture or stick a photograph in the middle of the frame.

Activity 18 Hot air balloon
Children decorate and cut out the balloon. They can cut it into segments along the thinner lines and try to reassemble it.

Activity 19 Gingerbread person
Children decorate and cut out the gingerbread person. If it is enlarged the ingredients can be listed on the back of it.

Activity 20 Caterpillars
Children decorate and cut out the caterpillars. They can cut out the segments and hinge them with fasteners so that the caterpillar wiggles.

Cutting and Assembling

Activity 21 Design a flag
Children design a flag (e.g. for their class or school) and assemble it following the guide at the bottom right of the sheet.

Activity 22 Standing spider
Children decorate and cut out the spider. They fold the end of each leg along the dotted line so that it can stand or hang from a thread. This works best photocopied onto thin card.

Activity 23 Space rocket
Children decorate and cut out the rocket's components, assembling them as shown at the bottom right of the sheet. The children can write a name for their rocket on its base.

Activity 24 Jeep
Children decorate and cut out the jeep's components. Assemble it as shown at the bottom right of the sheet. Design the jeep's number/license plate.

Cutting Along a Broken Line

Activity 25 Kite
Children decorate and cut out the pieces of the kite along the broken lines. Attach a string tail to the kite and stick the bows to it.

Activity 26 Car
Children decorate and cut out the car along the broken line. Draw a driver in the front window.

Activity 27 Elephant
Children decorate and cut out the elephant along the broken line. On a separate piece of paper draw a suitable background to stick the elephant onto.

Cutting Along a Dotted Line

Activity 28 Wizard's hat
Children cut along the dotted line to make a wizard's hat. Decorate the hat with other shapes or patterns.

Activity 29 Dinosaur
Children make a dinosaur by cutting along the dotted line. Decorate it and on a separate piece of paper draw a suitable background to stick it onto.

Activity 30 Ship
Children cut along the dotted line to make a ship. Decorate it and on a separate piece of paper paint a seascape to stick it onto.

Cutting and Assembling More Complex Shapes

Activity 31 Make an elephant
Children decorate and cut out each piece of the elephant. Assemble it as shown at the bottom right of the sheet. Stick down the body first, followed by the head and then the remaining features.

Activity 32 Make a pig
Children decorate and cut out each piece of the pig. Assemble it as shown at the bottom right of the sheet. The body should be stuck down first, followed by the head and then the remaining features.

Activity 33 Making breakfast
Children cut out the frying pan and the food. They stick the food onto the frying pan and write their breakfast for that day on the frying pan handle.

Activity 34 Make a flower
Children decorate and cut out the parts of the flower. Assemble them as shown at the bottom right of the sheet.

Activity 35 Standing crocodile
Children decorate and cut out the crocodile. Fold it along its length and fold its feet along the dotted lines. This will enable the crocodile to stand.

Activity 36 Packing a suitcase
Children decorate and cut out the suitcase and clothes. Stick the clothes onto the suitcase. On the back of the suitcase they may list other items they would pack for a journey.

Activity 37 Make a lion
Children decorate and cut out the pieces of the lion. Assemble them as shown at the bottom right of the sheet, with the legs being stuck down first.

Cutting Within Shapes
Activity 38 Butterfly
Children decorate the butterfly symmetrically and cut it out. Cut the marked circles from the wings and make the butterfly into a mobile.

Activity 39 Alien
Children decorate and cut out the alien. Carefully cut the shapes from its tummy. Attractive paper or fabric can be stuck behind these holes.

Activity 40 Wristwatch
Children decorate a watch and cut it out. Cut the buckle out and the watch can be worn over a sleeve.

Activity 41 Submarine
Children decorate and cut out the submarine. Cut around the circles to produce hinged portholes. On a separate piece of paper draw and cut out faces that can be stuck behind the hinged flaps.

Further Cutting Skills Activities

Cut out pictures from old greetings cards to use for a themed collage.

Cut out pictures and shapes from wrapping paper to explore patterns.

Cut out pictures from old magazines to use for sorting activities.

Use 2-D shapes as templates to make a shape picture from a given plan.

Children draw around their hands. Decorated and cut out these can be used as a border for a display.

Draw around shoes, cut out the templates and use them to investigate shoe sizes.

Cut out paper squares and use them to make a mosaic.

Fold a piece of paper into a concertina and cut out a row of paper figures.

Make some leaf rubbings and cut them out to use in an autumnal composition.

Cut out shapes with curved or straight sides and arrange them to make a pattern picture.

Design a scissor safety poster.

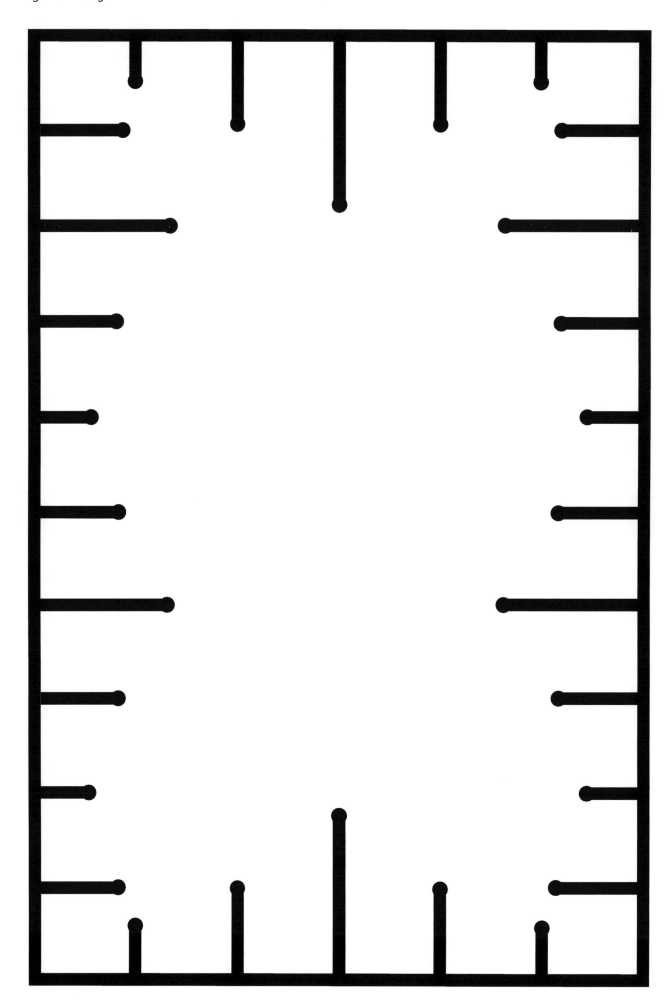

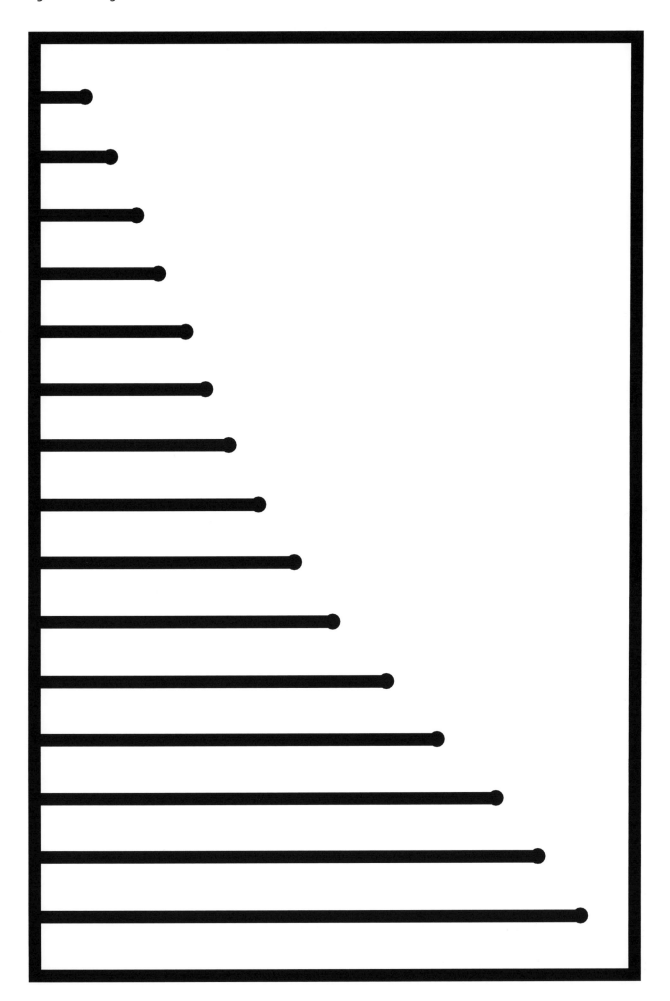

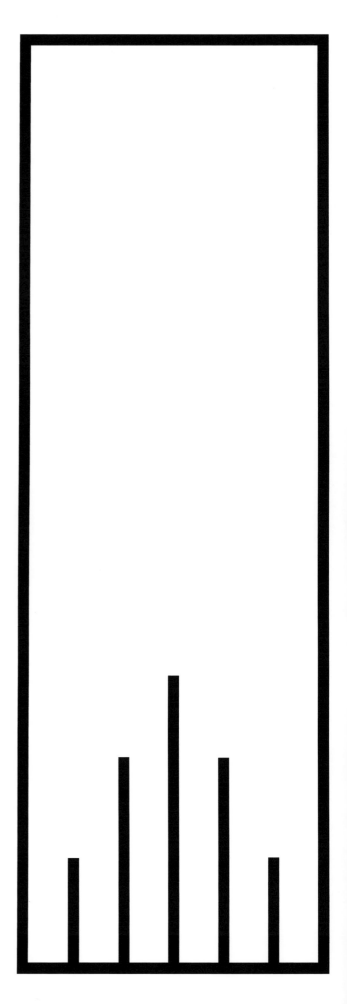

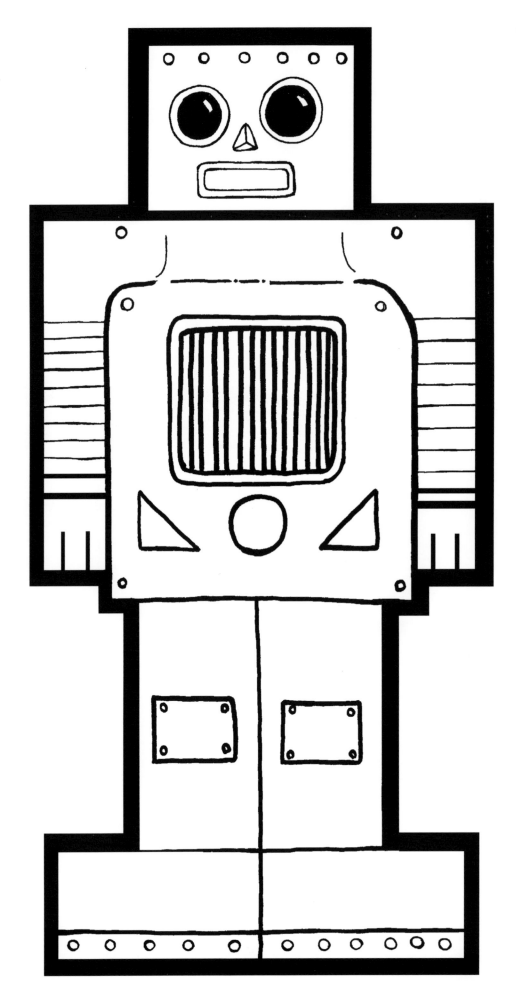

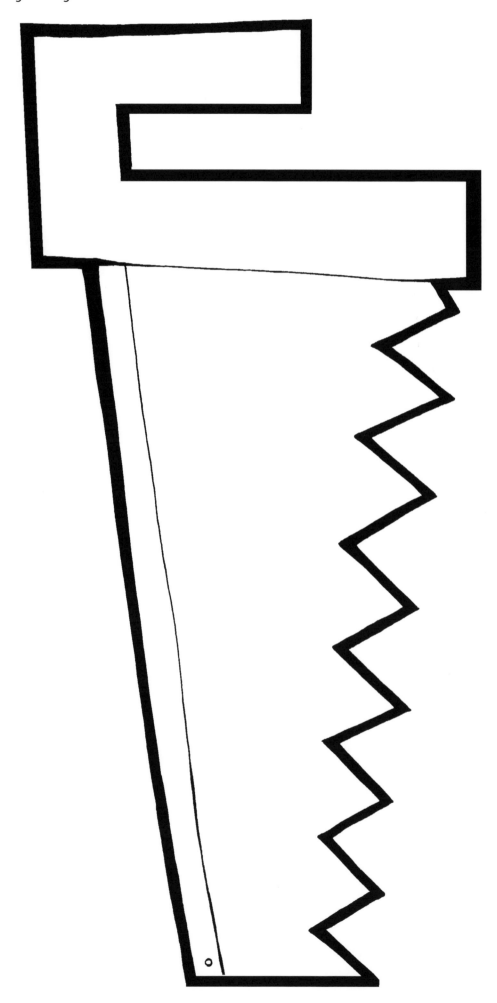

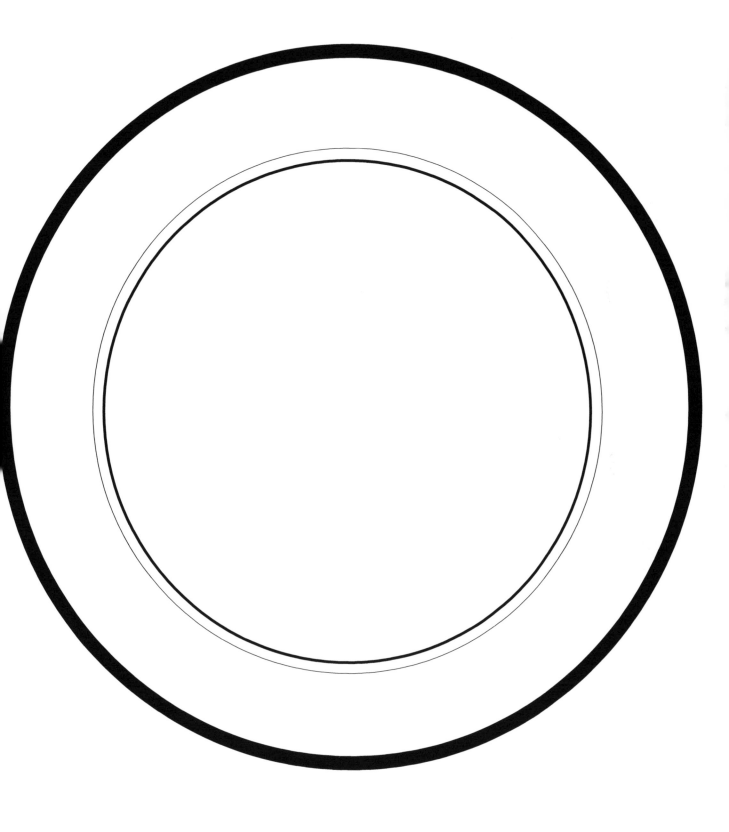

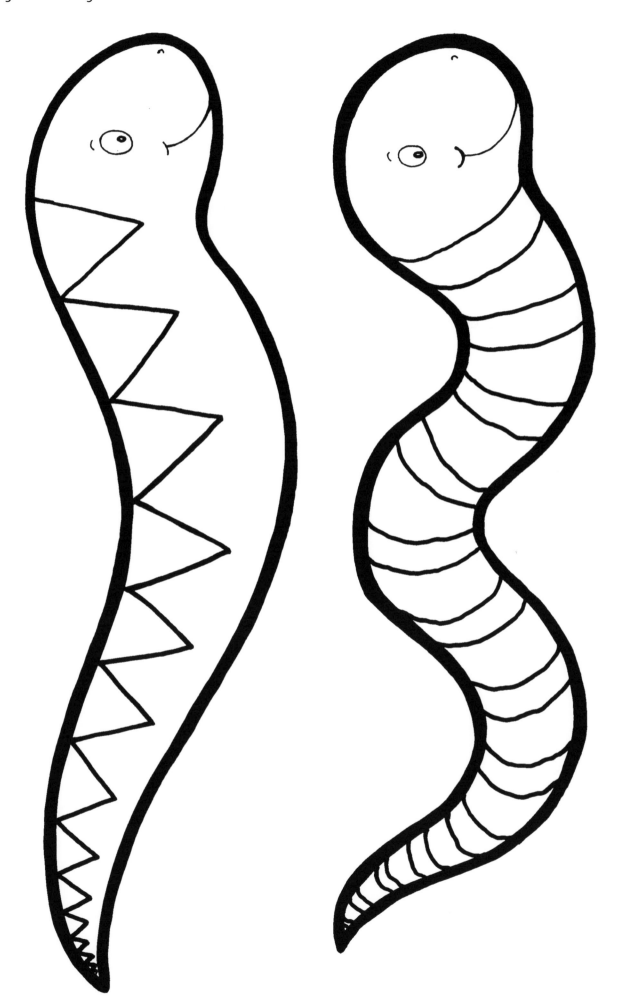

21

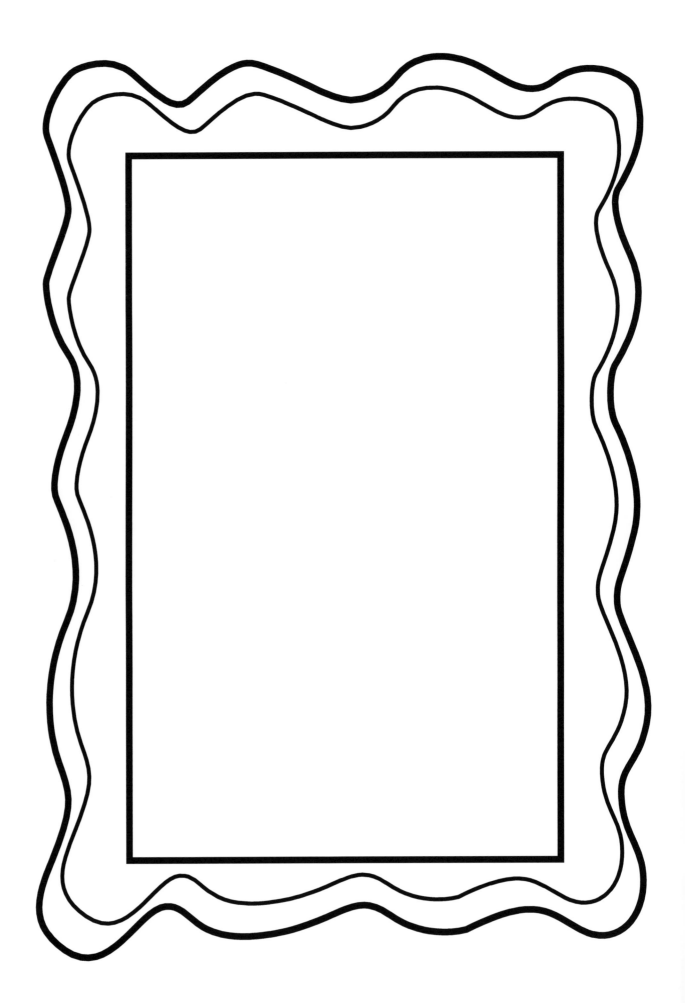

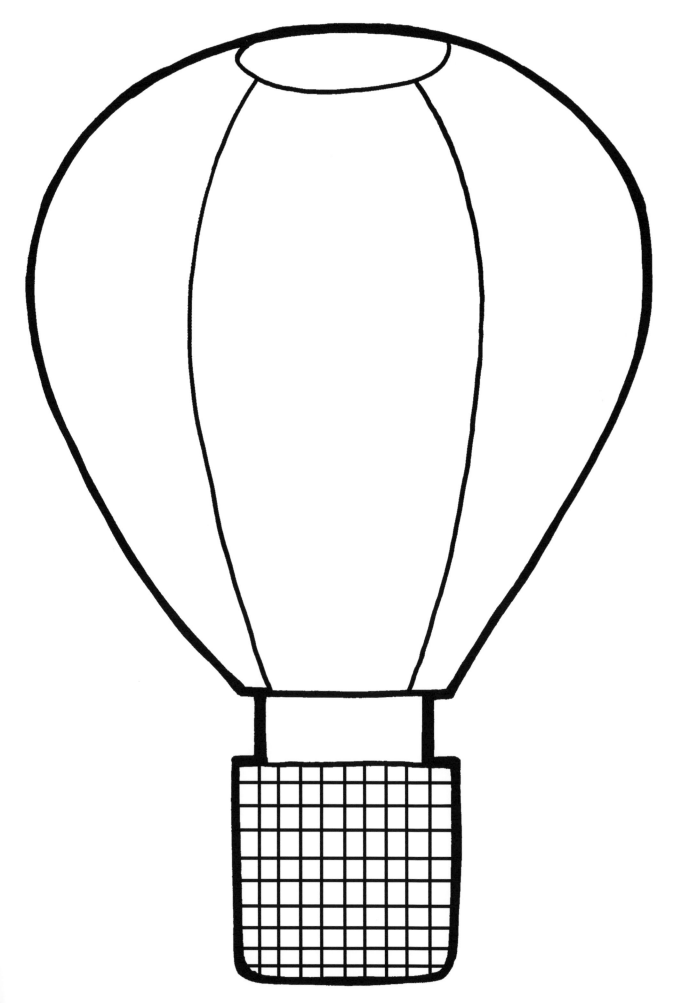

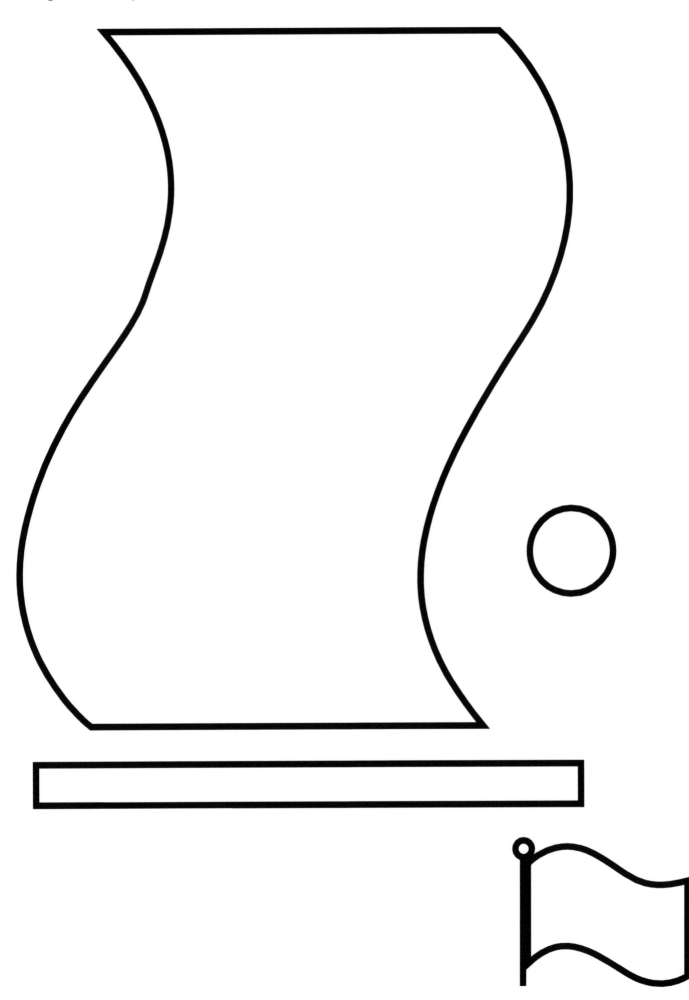

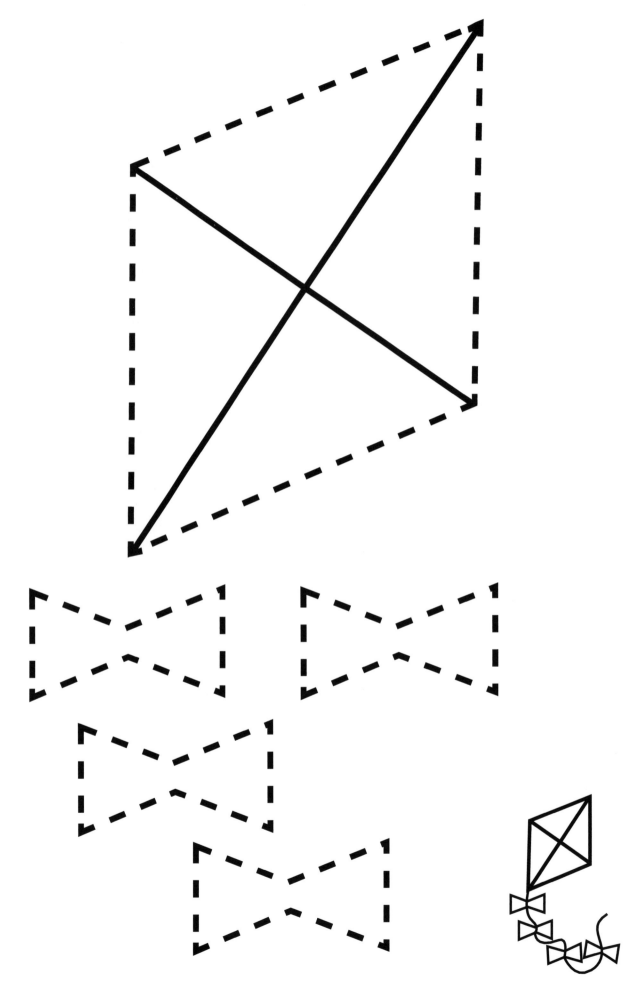

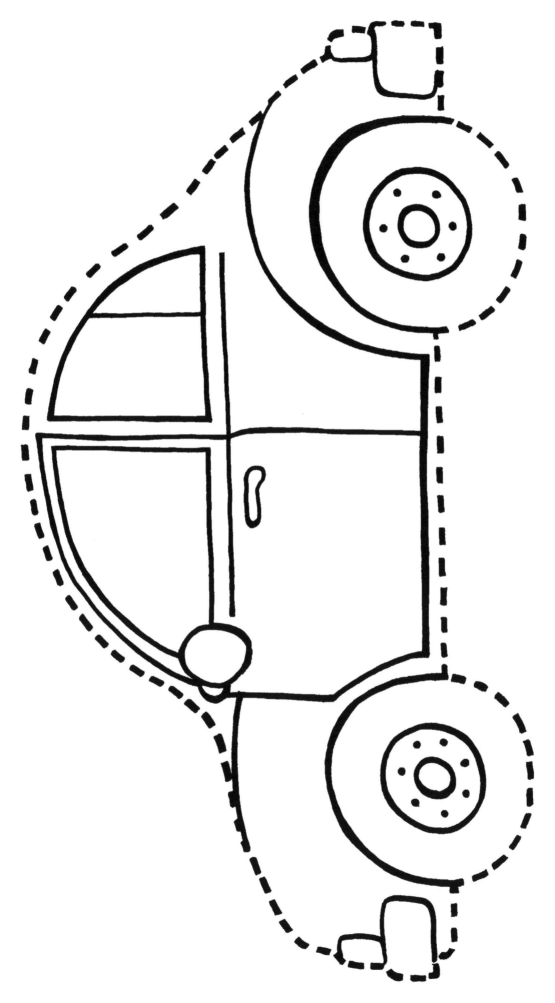

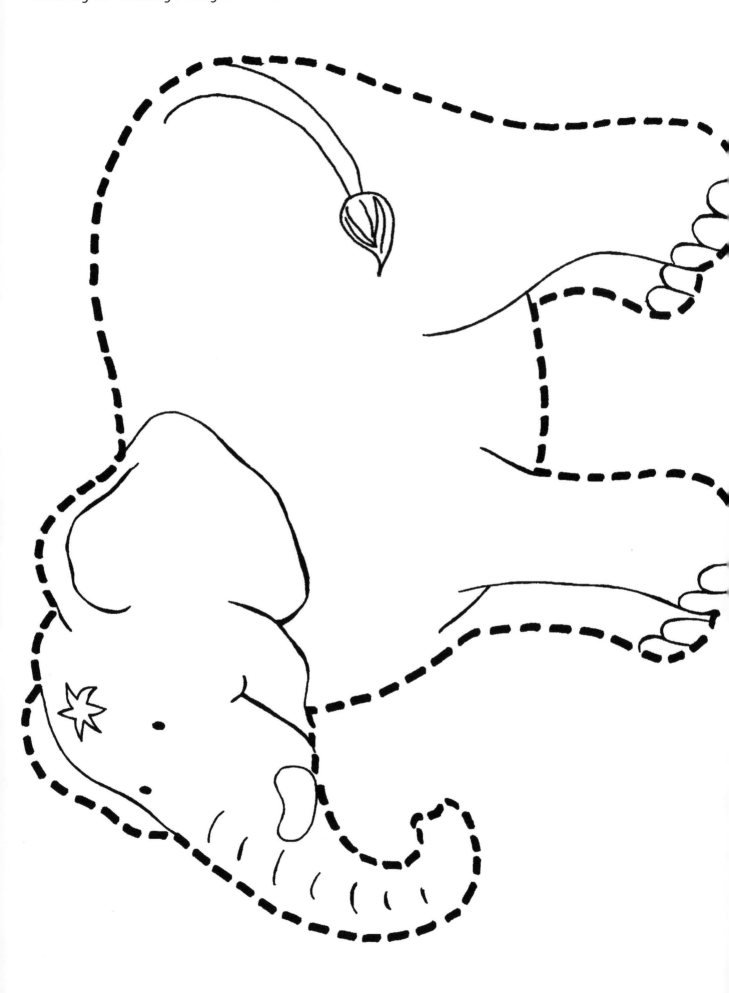

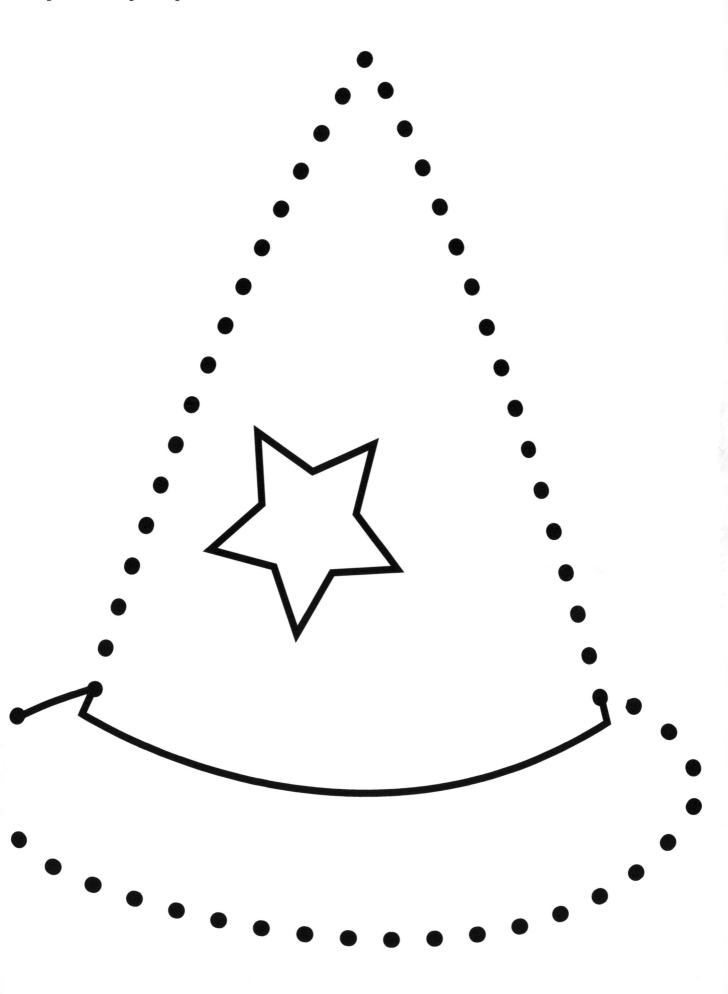

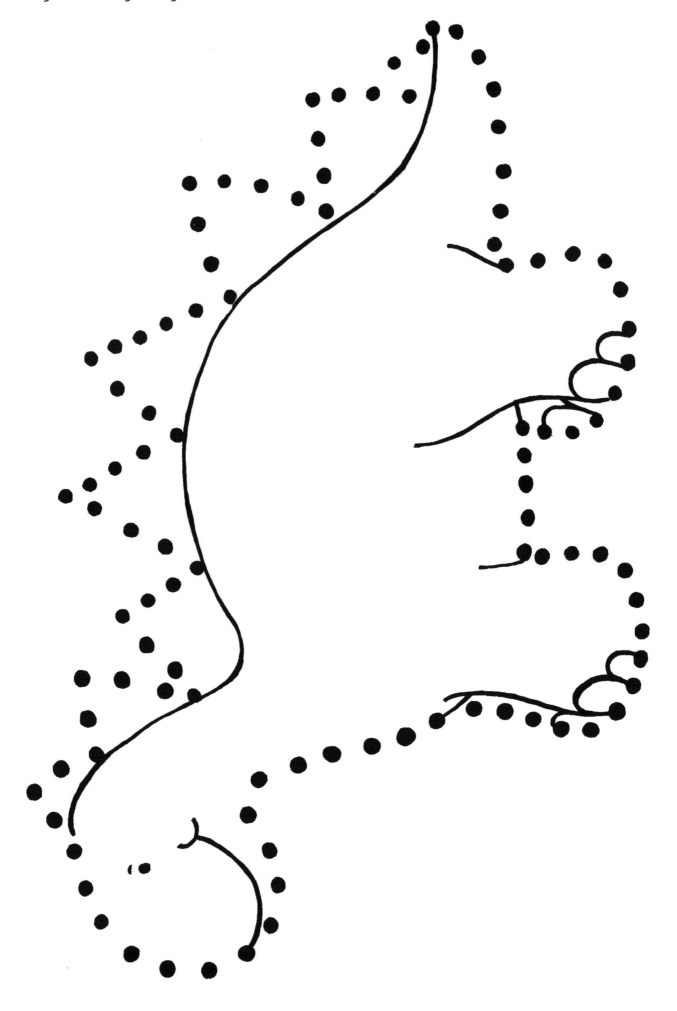

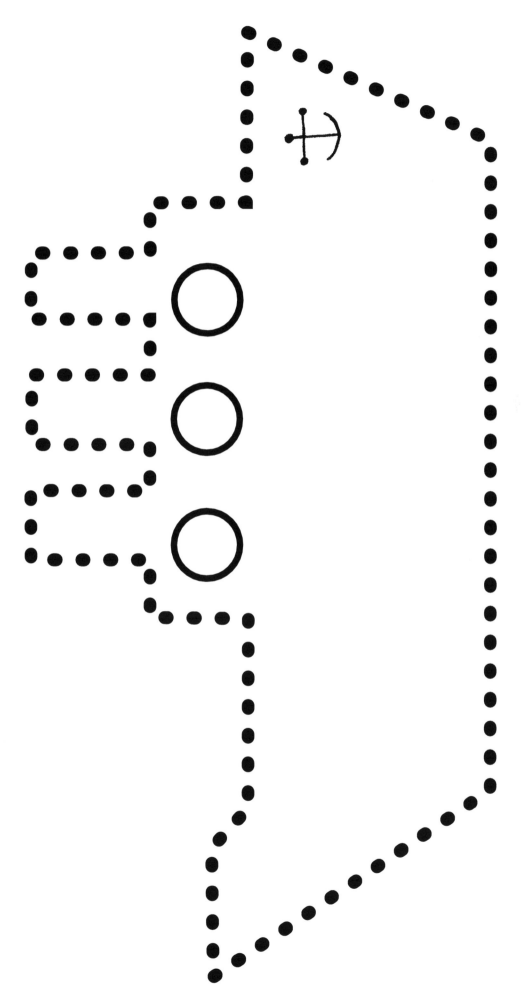

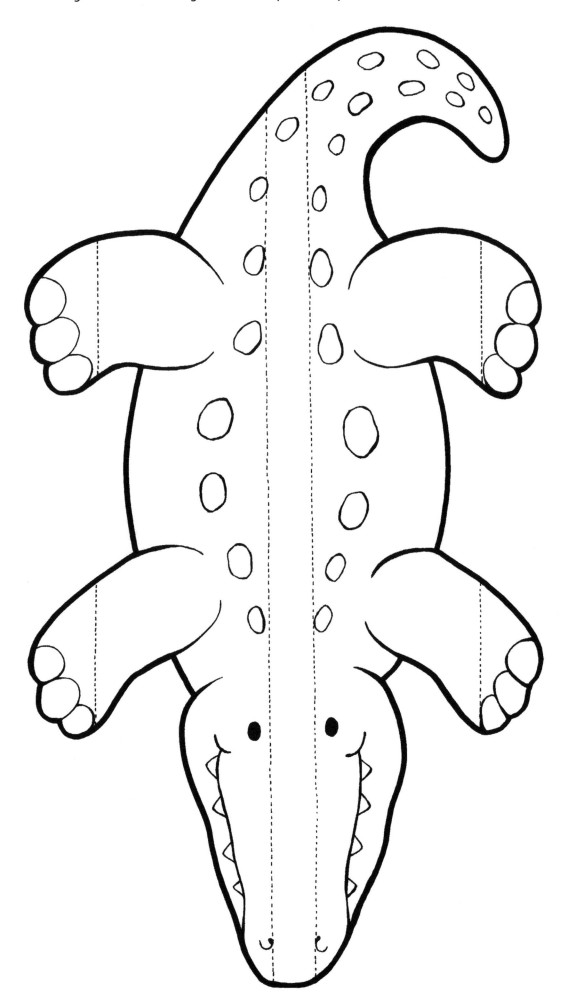

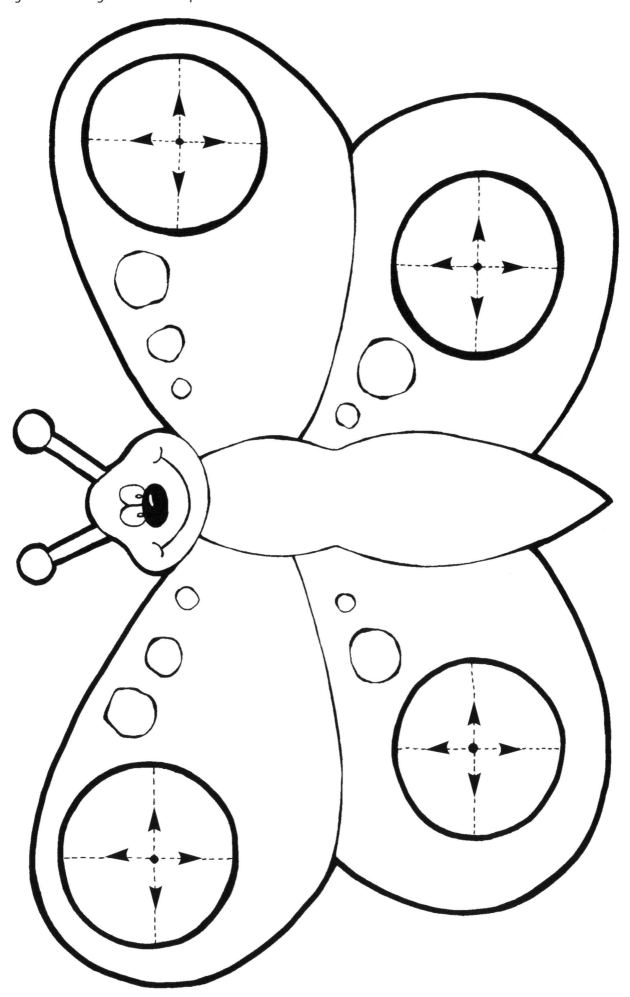

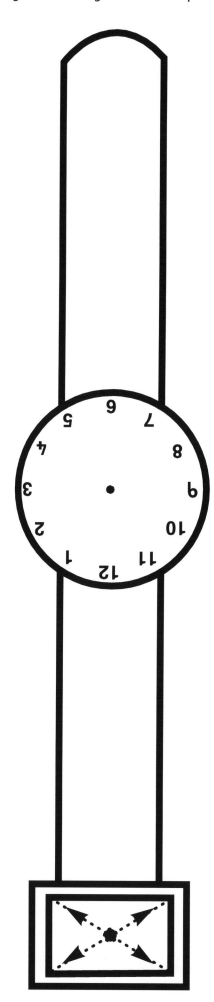

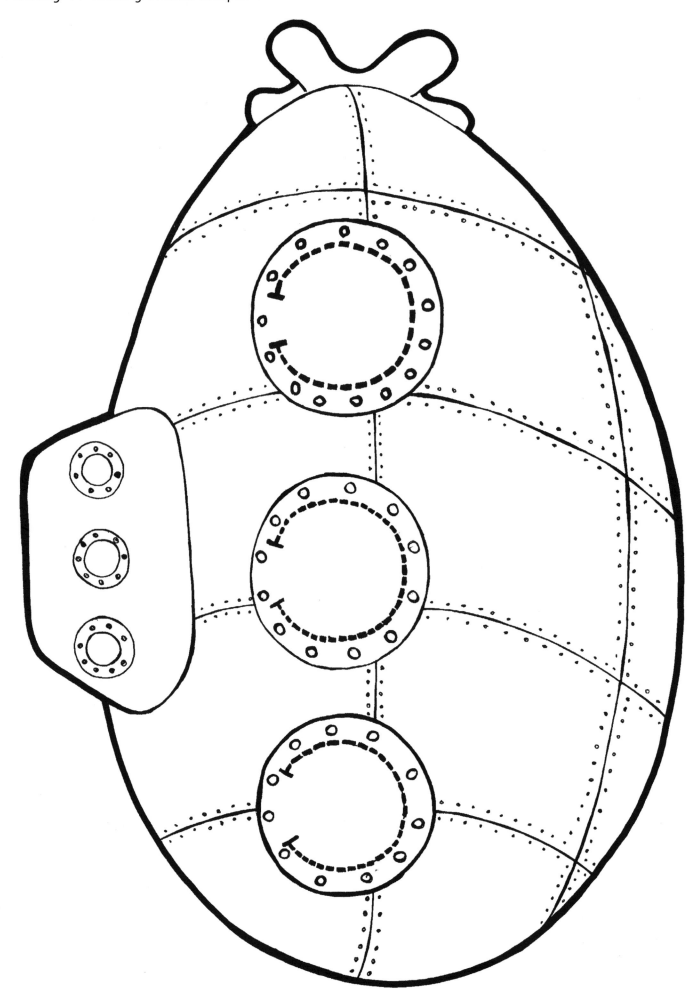